# Sticker Learn and Read

# Little Red Riding Hood

# How to use this book

**Sticker, Learn and Read** helps children to develop language and observational skills, as well as making reading enjoyable.

Read the stories with your child from start to finish. Encourage your child to point out the characters and actions in the illustrations, as they appear in the stories. This will help to develop observational and interaction skills.

Now read each page again, pointing to the sticker areas and ask your child to say the missing word or words. This will help to develop language skills. Then ask your child to find the correct stickers to complete the page. This will help to develop matching and hand-eye co-ordination skills.

Once all the stickers are in place on each page, read the page again, prompting your child to once again say the word or words associated with the stickers.

The learning and activity pages at the end of each story will help to encourage reading comprehension skills. Children will be prompted to scan text to locate information and to recall events.

One day Little Red Riding Hood was

taking a basket of  to her grandma.

cakes

She wore a red   and red  .

cape                              shoes

A  jumped from behind a  and

wolf                                                              tree

asked  where she was going. She told

Red Riding Hood

him she was going to visit her grandma.

The  wolf ran to Grandma's cottage where

there wàs smoke coming out of the chimney. He

knocked on the door and Grandma let him in.

4

The big, bad wolf locked  in a wardrobe.

Grandma

He dressed himself in Grandma's clothes and

put on her  before getting into  .

glasses                                              bed

5

When   arrived at Grandma's, she put

Red Riding Hood

the 🍪 in the kitchen and sat by the bed.

cakes

"What big 👀 you have," she said.

eyes

"Better to see you with," said the .

wolf

Red Riding Hood went closer to the

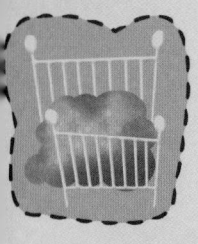. "What big 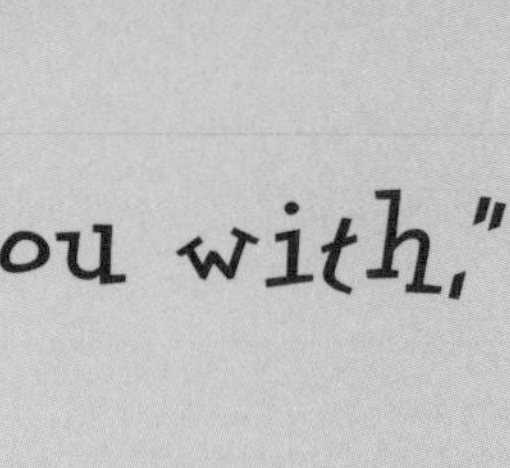 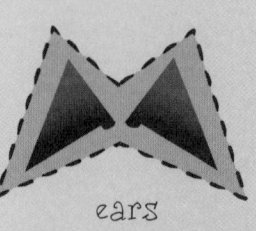 you have," she said.

bed                    ears

"Better to hear you with," said the   wolf .

Red Riding Hood went closer still. "Grandma,

what big 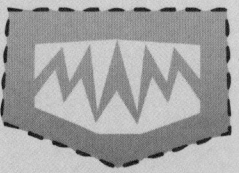 teeth you have!" she cried.

"Better to eat you with!" growled the wolf.

He leapt out of 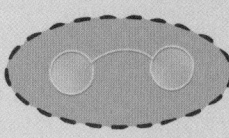 and the ⬭ fell off
bed                              glasses

his nose. 🧒 screamed as he chased her.
Red Riding Hood

9

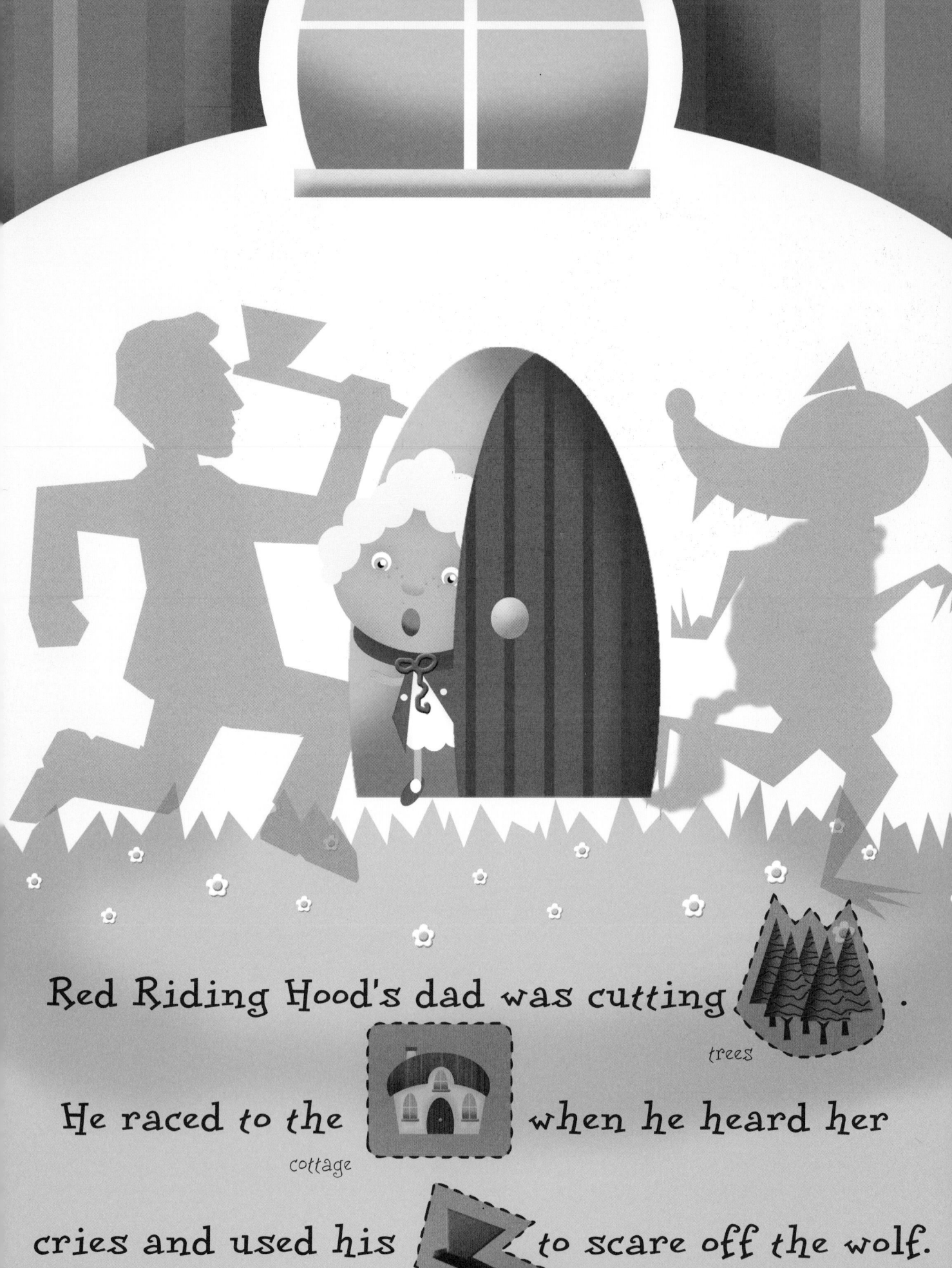

Red Riding Hood's dad was cutting  .

trees

He raced to the  when he heard her

cottage

cries and used his  to scare off the wolf.

axe

Red Riding Hood unlocked the 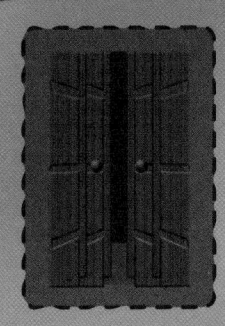 and

wardrobe

let Grandma out. They were safe! They had

a  of  to celebrate.

plate                cakes

11

## Which of these items was Red Riding Hood wearing?
## Find the stickers and circle the correct answers.

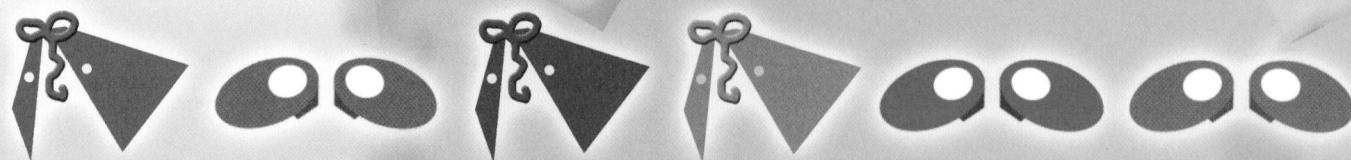

| Place your sticker here. | Place your sticker here. | Place your sticker here. | Place your sticker here. | Place your sticker here. | Place your sticker here. |

## Who was Red Riding Hood going to visit?
## Find the word sticker.

| Place your sticker here. |

## Why do you think Red Riding Hood was going on the visit?

_____

_____

_____

## Draw what she took with her.

## Who jumped out from behind a tree?
## Find the letter stickers to spell the word.

| Place your sticker here. | Place your sticker here. | Place your sticker here. | Place your sticker here. |

Choose the correct word to complete each sentence, then find the stickers.

friendly    happy
beautiful    bad    boastful

The big, [Place your sticker here.] wolf locked Grandma in a wardrobe.

jumped    crept
danced    tiptoed    galloped

A wolf [Place your sticker here.] from behind the trees.

laughed    screamed
giggled    moaned    slept

When the wolf leapt out of bed, Red Riding Hood [Place your sticker here.] .

cakes    bread    vegetables
grapes    nothing

To celebrate their safety, Red Riding Hood, her dad and Grandma ate [Place your sticker here.] .

What shapes were on Grandma's nightgown? Find the word sticker.

Place your sticker here.

Draw them back on!

Where did the wolf put Grandma? Find the letter stickers to spell the answer.

| Place your sticker here. | Place your sticker here. | Place your sticker here. | Place your sticker here. | Place your sticker here. | Place your sticker here. | Place your sticker here. | Place your sticker here. |
|---|---|---|---|---|---|---|---|

Which of these things did Red Riding Hood think looked big on Grandma? Circle the correct answers.

eyes        slippers

teeth        feet

nightie        ears

glasses

# Grandma's special cakes

 You will need a grown up to help you make your cakes.

**YOU WILL NEED:**
- kitchen scales • clear plastic bag • rolling pin
- wooden spoon • saucepan • greaseproof paper
- scissors • shallow baking tray • metal spoon
- knife

**INGREDIENTS:**
250g (8.8oz) digestive sweetened (wholemeal) biscuits
50g (1.7oz) butter plus a little for greasing
3 tablespoons golden syrup
200g (7oz) plain (dark) chocolate

**1** Tip the biscuits into a plastic bag. Seal it tightly.

**2** Use a rolling pin to crush the biscuits until they look like breadcrumbs.

**3** Ask an adult to place the butter, chocolate and syrup in a pan and heat gently until they have melted.

**4** Ask an adult to take the saucepan off the heat, stir in the crushed biscuits and mix well.

**5** Grease and line the baking tray with the greaseproof paper. Now pour the chocolatey mixture into it.

**6** Smooth the top of the mixture with a metal spoon until it's flat. Leave it to set.

**7** Cut the cake into bars while the mixture is still warm. Put the tray into the fridge for about two hours to finish cooling off.

15

Unscramble these words. Find the word stickers and draw lines to match them to the pictures.

olwf

Place your sticker here.

ttcaego

Place your sticker here.

deb

Place your sticker here.

ksace

Place your sticker here.

yese

Place your sticker here.

16

# What's the time Mr. Wolf?

Here's a fun game for you to play with a group of friends. Choose a player to be Mr. Wolf. Mr. Wolf stands at one side of the room and faces the wall. The rest of the players stand at the other side of the room and, in chorus, shout out, "What's the time Mr. Wolf?". Mr. Wolf answers with a time ending in "o'clock". For example, three o'clock. The other players will then take three steps forward. Once everyone has stepped forward, they repeat the question again. This continues until Mr. Wolf shouts, "DINNER TIME!", at which point the wolf turns around and tries to catch another player as they run back to the starting place. If the wolf manages to touch another player, that player then becomes the wolf in the next game.

## Have fun!

# Which of these sentences is correct?

1. Red Riding Hood took Grandma some bread.

2. The wolf was hiding behind Grandma's cottage when he jumped out at Red Riding Hood.

3. Red Riding Hood was going to visit her dad.

4. The big bad wolf locked Grandma in the cellar.

5. Red Riding Hood put the cakes in the kitchen and sat down next to the bed.

6. Red Riding Hood looked closer and noticed that Grandma's bed was a lot bigger.

Write a word that best describes Red Riding Hood.

Write a word that best describes the wolf.

# How many differences can you find between these pictures?

There are [Place your sticker here.] differences.

19

# Use the number stickers to put these pictures in the correct story order.

a.

Place your sticker here.

b.

Place your sticker here.

c.

Place your sticker here.

d.

Place your sticker here.

e.

Place your sticker here.

f.

Place your sticker here.

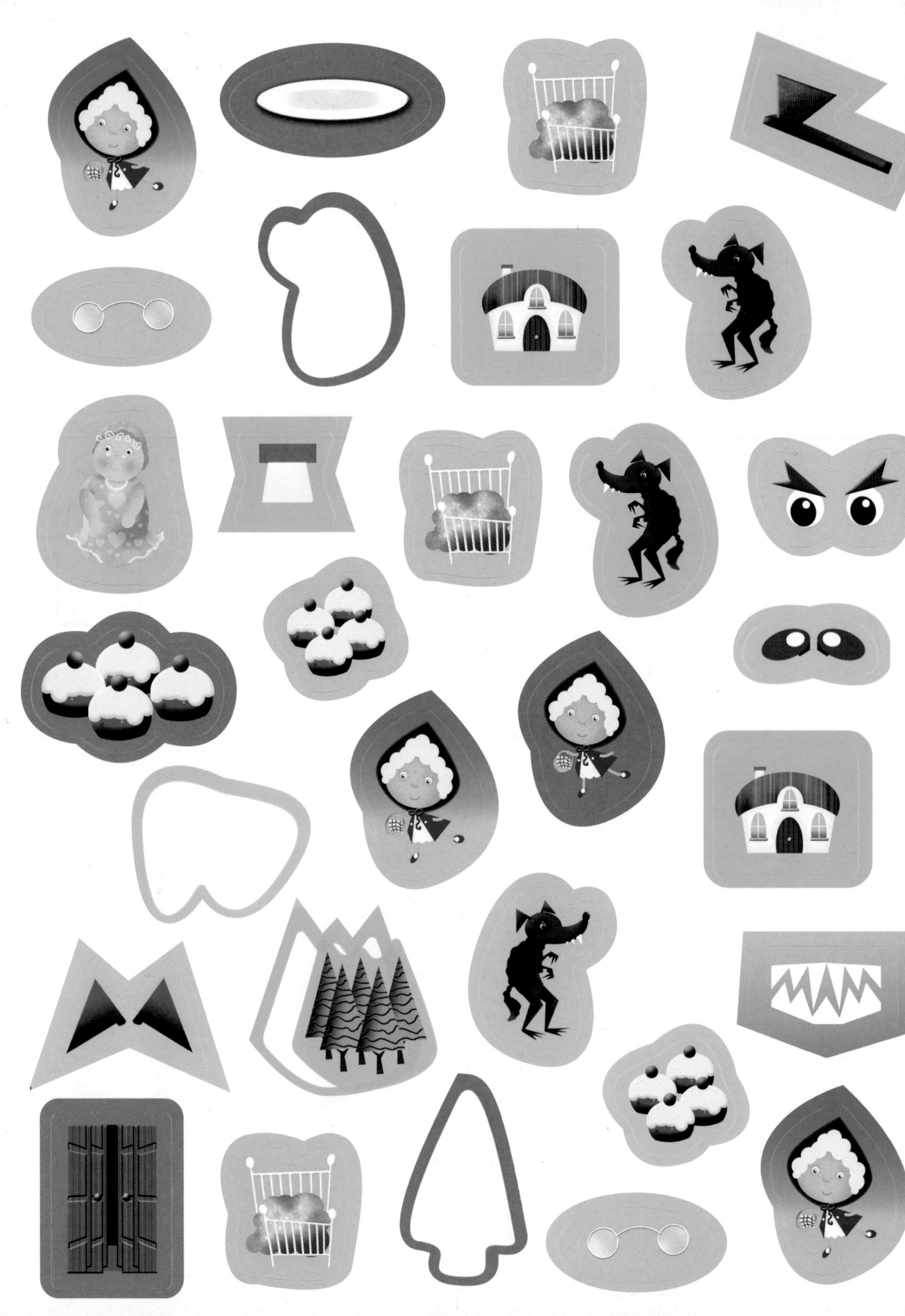

red cape

blue shoes

purple cape

hearts

green cape

red shoes

purple shoes

Grandma

bad

1

cakes

jumped

screamed

2

w

o

l

f

3

w

a

r

d

4

r

o

b

e

5

wolf

6

eyes

cottage

cakes

bed

6

# Sticker
## Learn and Read

# Cinderella

Cinderella lived in a house with her two lazy stepsisters. Every day, Cinderella put on an apron and did all the housework.

Cinderella cleaned the floor with a  and

mop

cooked pasta in a  on the stove.

pan

Meanwhile, the stepsisters ate .

cakes

One day a special  arrived.
letter

A handsome  had invited Cinderella
prince

and her stepsisters to a party at the .
palace

The  told Cinderella she was too busy

stepsisters

to go. She had to use the  to smooth

iron

out the creases in their party  .

dresses

Just then, Cinderella's  appeared. fairy godmother

She waved her magic  and turned wand

Cinderella's rags into a beautiful . gown

26

The fairy godmother waved her 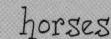 again and

wand

turned a pumpkin and *two* mice into a golden

 pulled by beautiful white 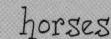 .

carriage                                                    horses

27

At the party, Cinderella and the prince danced

Cinderella

together all night. The prince wore a golden

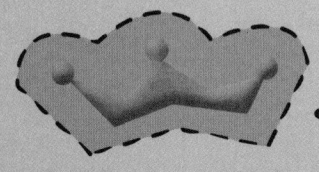 and Cinderella a sparkly .

crown

tiara

When the  ⏰ struck midnight, the

clock,

magic ended. Cinderella grabbed her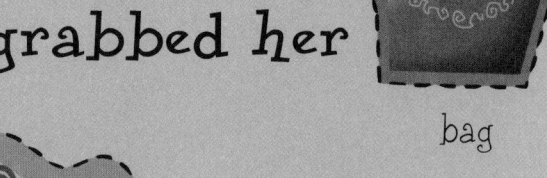

bag

and ran home losing a 👟 on the way.

shoe

The prince placed the dainty shoe on a velvet

 and searched for  . When he

cushion

Cinderella

found her, the [shoe] was a perfect fit!

shoe

The prince gave Cinderella a  and asked

her to marry him. Now Cinderella was a

princess with a  and a handsome  .

Find the missing word
and picture stickers and then find
the words from the story in the
wordsearch grid.
You can read across and down.

```
E K P J G K L M P E U T I
G I R N O T R E A S W P E
Z C I N D E R E L L A T V
A I N M M O A U A I N R J
F I C H O B O V C L D K T
H Q E E T R T I E U S S A
S T A O H S R M T K R Y T
I H S T E P S I S T E R E
B I N V R T A T M O P E S
S N N V I L E T T E R E N
```

32

How many lazy stepsisters were there?
Find the number sticker.

What did Cinderella use to clean the floor?
Find the missing letter stickers.

Circle the word you think best
describes how Cinderella felt
when the stepsisters left.

happy

sad

angry

Why?

_____

_____

_____

Why do you think the stepsisters were mean to Cinderella?

_____

_____

_____

_____

_____

Who invited Cinderella and her sisters to a party at the palace? Find the missing letter stickers to spell the word.

| Place your sticker here. | Place your sticker here. | Place your sticker here. | Place your sticker here. | Place your sticker here. | Place your sticker here. |
| --- | --- | --- | --- | --- | --- |

What did Cinderella lose when she ran home from the party? Find the letter stickers to spell the word.

| Place your sticker here. | Place your sticker here. | Place your sticker here. | Place your sticker here. |
| --- | --- | --- | --- |

Draw the missing hands on the clock to show the time that Cinderella had to leave the party.

# What do you think the prince's letter inviting Cinderella and her stepsisters to the party looked like? Find the missing stickers to help you.

Place your
sticker here.

Place your
sticker here.

Place your
sticker here.

Place your
sticker here.

# Use the number stickers to put these pictures in the correct story order.

a.

Place your sticker here.

b.

Place your sticker here.

c.

Place your sticker here.

d.

Place your sticker here.

e.

Place your sticker here.

f.

Place your sticker here.

37

The clock has struck midnight! Help Cinderella get back to her coach and horses.

Which of these sentences is correct?

1. Cinderella wanted to go too the ball. ☐

2. Cinderella wanted to go two the ball. ☐

3. Cinderella wanted to go to the ball. ☐

38

Choose the correct word
to complete each sentence,
then find the stickers.

handsome    funny

ugly    sad

Cinderella married the

Place your
sticker here.    prince.

cakes    vegetables

pizza    fruit

While Cinderella cooked and
cleaned, the stepsisters
ate
Place your
sticker here.    .

sit-ups    housework

painting    ballet

Every day Cinderella
put on an apron and
did
Place your
sticker here.    .

39

# Write your own fairy tale.
## Don't forget to plan a beginning, middle and an end.

_____

_____

_____

_____

_____

_____

_____

_____

_____

_____

_____

_____

_____

_____

**The End.**

| PRINCE | LETTER | STEPSISTER | MOP |

| CINDERELLA | WAND | PALACE | GODMOTHER |

| 2 | m | o | p |

| p | r | i | n |

| c | e | s | h | o | e |

| 1 | 2 | 3 | 4 | 5 | 6 |

| handsome | cakes | housework |

| Dear: | Where: |

| From: | When: |

# Sticker
## Learn and Read

# Sleeping Beauty

Once upon a time, a  and  had

king       queen

a baby princess. They invited their friends

to a big party at the 🏰 to celebrate.

castle

Three good  fairies , carrying magic  wands

came with  presents for the princess. A fourth

fairy, who wasn't invited, was very angry.

She told the  and  that when the

king        queen

princess was eighteen, she would prick her

finger on a  and fall asleep forever.

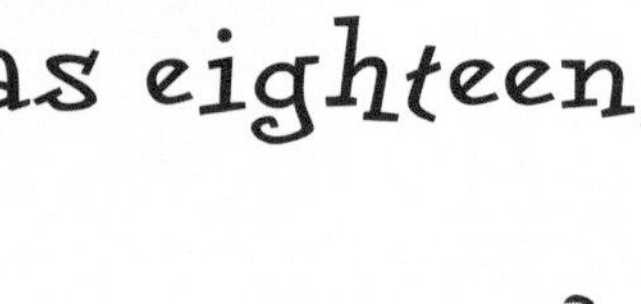

needle

The queen burst into  . The king

ordered all of the ✕ to be destroyed. A 🔥

raged as wooden spinning wheels were burned.

tears

needles

fire

One day, eighteen years later, the  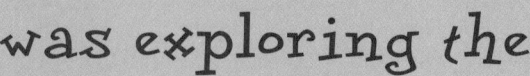 princess

was exploring the 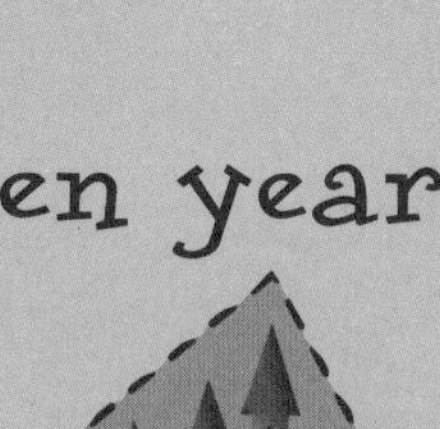 castle. She climbed some

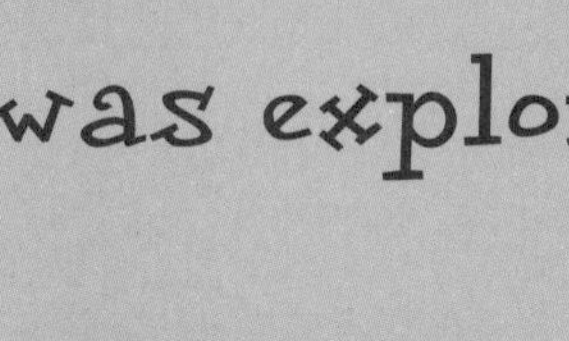

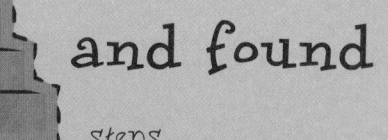 and found an old woman sewing.

steps

The old woman got up out of her .
chair

She gave her  to the  who pricked
needle                              princess

her finger on it and fell to the floor.

The  and queen were heartbroken when

king

they found the princess. They carried her to

and called for the three 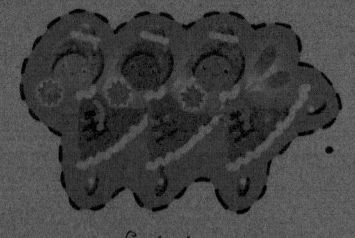.

bed

fairies

48

The fairies waved their  and sent

wands

everyone to sleep. The princess's  and

cat

the  in the fields were soon all asleep.

cows

One hundred years later, a handsome prince rode by on his horse. He cut his way through the thick vines to the castle door.

He found the  and kissed her. Sleeping
princess

Beauty woke up! The gave her a ,
prince                                    ring

and they married and lived happily ever after.

How many good fairies were there in the story? Find the number sticker.

Place your sticker here.

**fairies**

Find the word stickers and circle what the fairies brought to the princess's party.

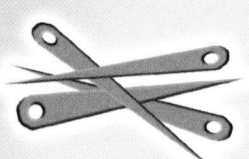

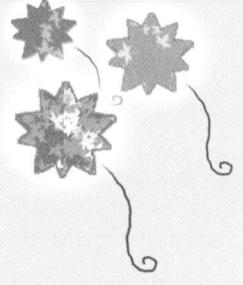

Place your sticker here.

Place your sticker here.

Place your sticker here.

Place your sticker here.

Where did the king and queen hold their party? Find the letter stickers to spell the word.

Place your sticker here.

Place your sticker here.

Place your sticker here.

Place your sticker here.

Place your sticker here.

Place your sticker here.

Who wasn't invited to the party?
Find the picture sticker.

How did this make her feel? Why?

_____

_____

_____

_____

What did the bad fairy say the princess would
prick her finger on? Find the letter
stickers to spell the word.

| Place your sticker here. | Place your sticker here. | Place your sticker here. | Place your sticker here. | Place your sticker here. | Place your sticker here. |
|---|---|---|---|---|---|

How old did the bad fairy say the
princess would be when she pricked
her finger? Find the word sticker.

| Place your sticker here. |
|---|

**years old**

# How many years did everyone sleep for?
## Find the word sticker.

Place your
sticker here.

# years

## Help the prince find the right path to
## rescue Sleeping Beauty.

a

b

c

Place your sticker here.

needles

Can you write this part of the story in your own words?

_____

_____

_____

_____

# Find the stickers and circle the odd one out in each row.

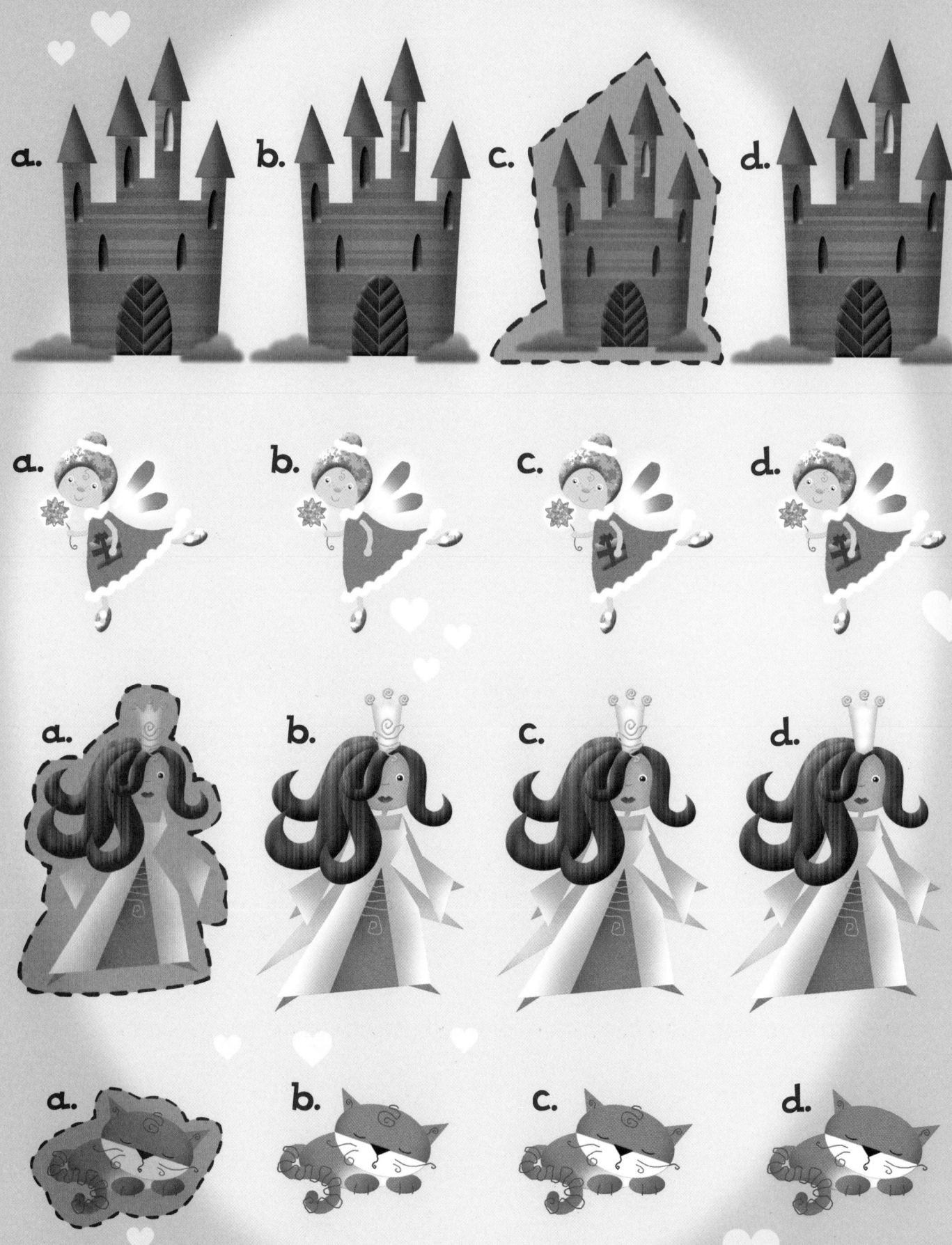

# Use the number stickers to put these pictures in the correct story order.

a.

Place your sticker here.

b.

Place your sticker here.

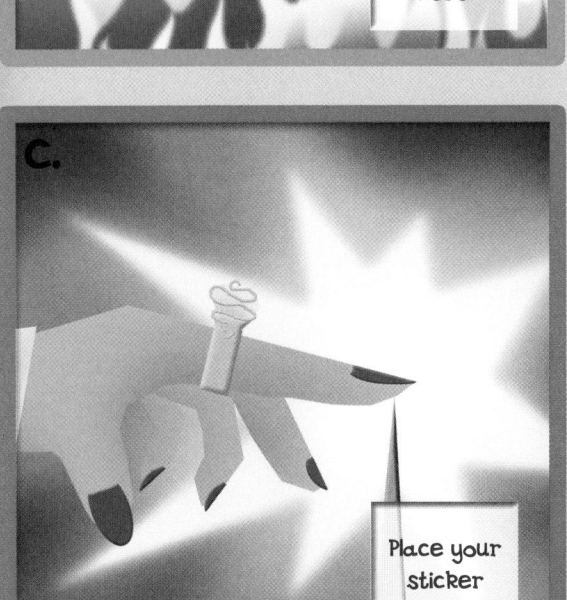

c.

Place your sticker here.

d.

Place your sticker here.

e.

Place your sticker here.

f.

Place your sticker here.

# Make your own fairy wings

**YOU WILL NEED:**
- sheet of card
- ruler · pencil
- scissors · glue
- pen · ribbon
- net or shiny fabric

**1** Ask an adult to cut out a rectangle of card measuring at least 22cm × 38cm (8½in × 15in). Draw a large pair of wings on your card.

 You will need a grown-up to help you make your wings.

**2** Ask an adult to cut out the wings and then carefully trim out the shape in the middle, leaving a frame at least 1.5cm (½in) thick all the way around. Now glue all around the edge of the frame.

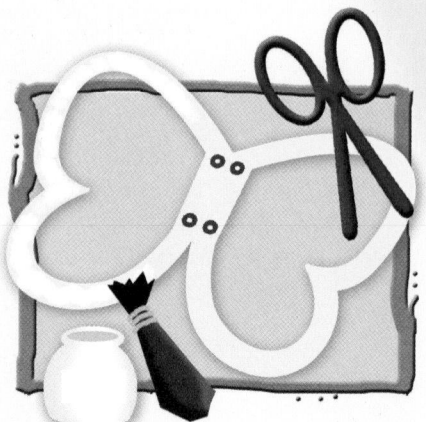

**3** Stretch out the netting or fabric and lay it onto the glued frame so that it is stuck in place.

**4** When the glue is dry, neatly cut around the edge of the wings to trim off the extra fabric.

**5** Ask an adult to make four holes in the middle section of the wings. Thread two pieces of ribbon through the holes to make pretty straps.

**6** Decorate your wings with stickers or paint on cute spots and flowers.

## Which of the following is a complete sentence?

a. The princess for one hundred years.

b. The princess slept for one hundred years.

c. The princess slept by.

d. The princess was very.

e. The princess was tired of.

## How did the prince wake up Sleeping Beauty?

He | Place your sticker here. | Place your sticker here. | Place your sticker here. | Place your sticker here. | Place your sticker here. | Place your sticker here. | her.

59

# What do you think happened after the story ended?

_____

_____

_____

_____

_____

_____

_____

_____

_____

_____

_____

_____

_____

_____

_____

_____

3    eighteen    6

one hundred

needles    wands    ring    presents

c a s t l e

n e e d l e

k i s s e d

1    2    3    4    5    6

# Sticker
## Learn and Read

# The Frog Prince

Once upon a time there lived a  who
princess

owned a golden  . She loved to play near
ball

the  , throwing and catching the ball.
castle

One day *the* princess was playing by *the*

flowers

when she threw the 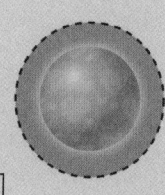 over her
ball

 and into the pond.

crown

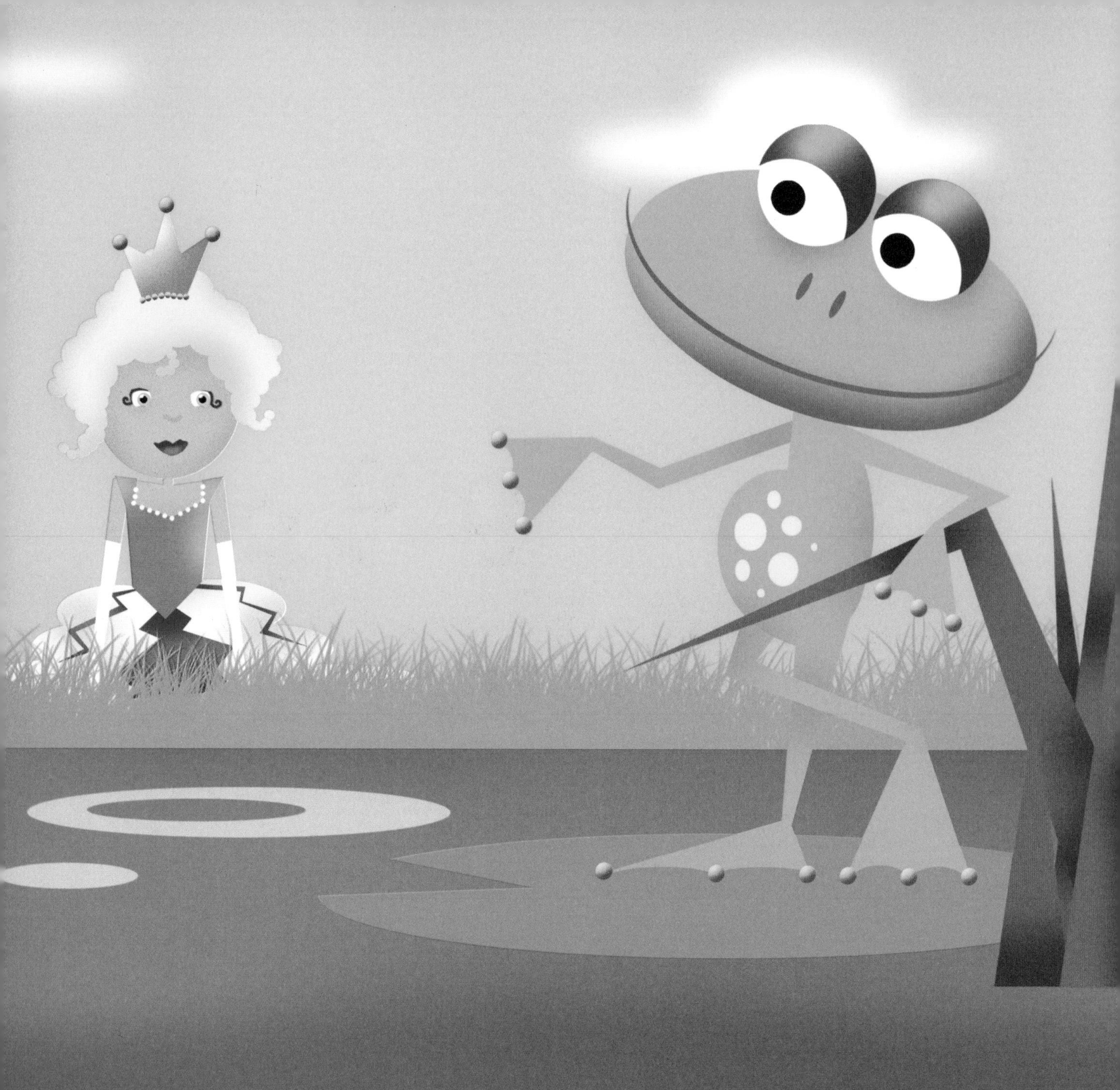

The princess was crying for her 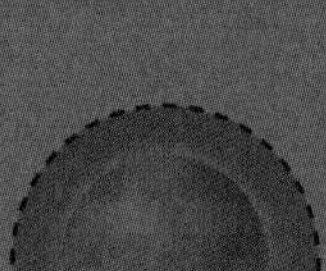 ball when a

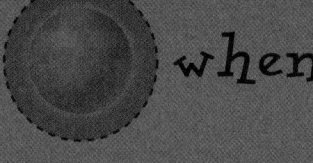

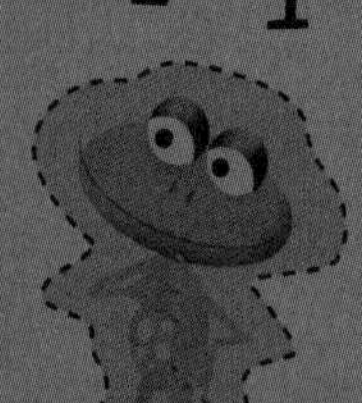 frog appeared and said, "If you give me a

reward, I'll get your ball."

"What do you want?" asked the  . "I want

princess

to eat from your golden  and sleep on

plate

your silken  for three nights," he said.

pillow

65

The  ready to agree to anything to get

princess

her ⬤ back, wiped away her 💧 and said,

ball                                   tears

"Yes, I promise you can do those things."

The  dived to the bottom of the pond,

which was filled with  and returned with

the golden ball. The  was delighted.

frog

fish

princess

Later that day the  knocked at the

frog

castle

door. "Remember your promise to me, ?"

princess

"Oh no! It's you," the princess cried.

For three nights the  had to share her

princess

with the frog and let him sleep on a

food

silken  in her bed.

pillow

The knew that the hated him.

frog                                                    princess

He began to cry. "I only wanted to be your

friend," he said. This made the princess sad.

The  was sorry and kissed the frog,

princess

breaking a  evil spell. Suddenly the

witch's

 turned into a handsome .

frog                                    prince

What did the princess lose in the pond?
Find the letter stickers to spell the words.

| Place your sticker here. | Place your sticker here. | Place your sticker here. | Place your sticker here. |

What creature offered to help the princess?

| Place your sticker here. | Place your sticker here. | Place your sticker here. | Place your sticker here. |

Which two things did the princess have to share with
the frog? Find the word stickers that match the
pictures and circle the correct answers.

| Place your sticker here. | Place your sticker here. | Place your sticker here. | Place your sticker here. | Place your sticker here. |

# Find the missing word and picture stickers and then find the words in the wordsearch grid.

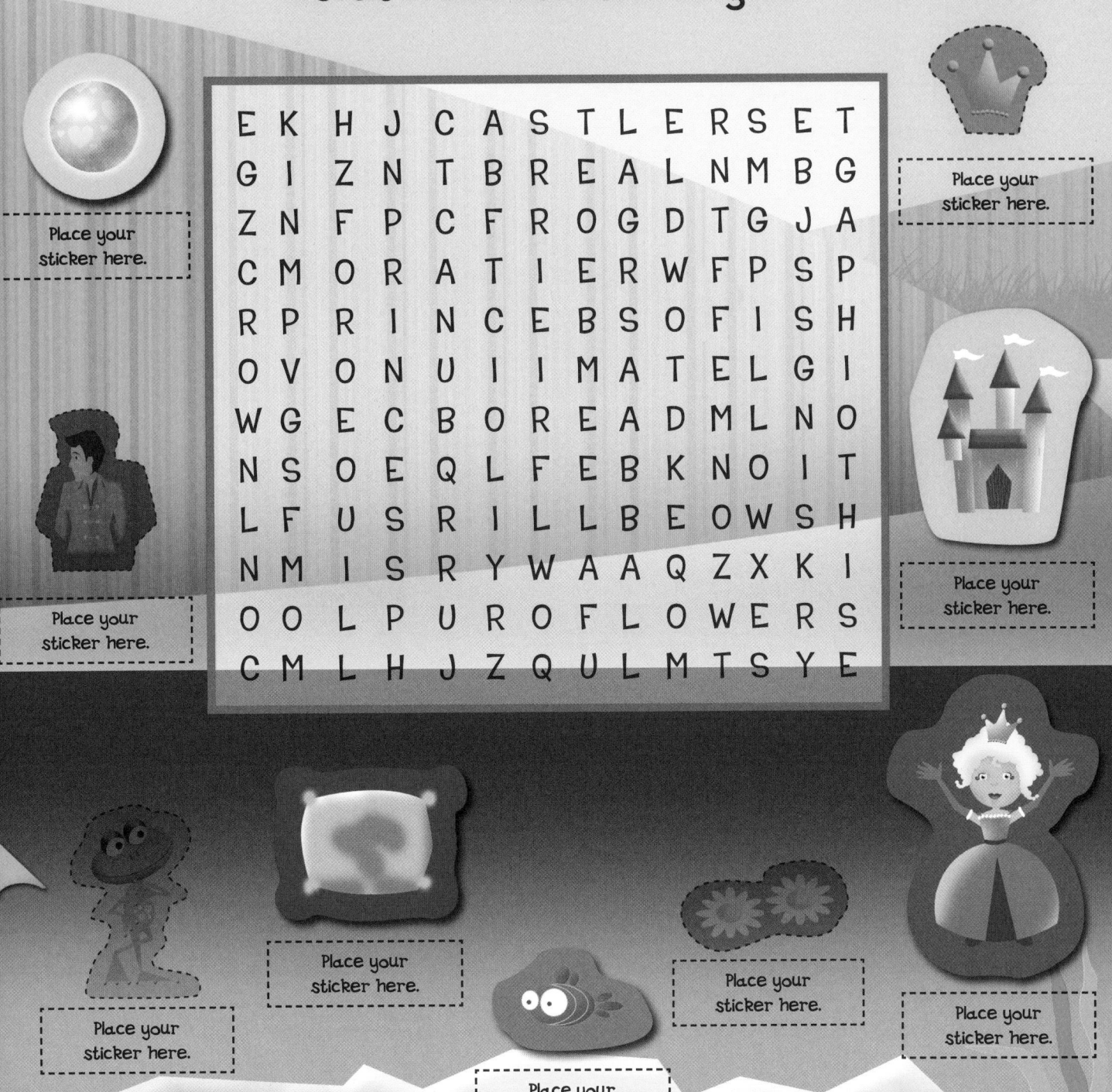

Place your sticker here.

Place your sticker here.

Place your sticker here.

Place your sticker here.

Place your sticker here.

Place your sticker here.

Place your sticker here.

Place your sticker here.

Place your sticker here.

| E | K | H | J | C | A | S | T | L | E | R | S | E | T |
| G | I | Z | N | T | B | R | E | A | L | N | M | B | G |
| Z | N | F | P | C | F | R | O | G | D | T | G | J | A |
| C | M | O | R | A | T | I | E | R | W | F | P | S | P |
| R | P | R | I | N | C | E | B | S | O | F | I | S | H |
| O | V | O | N | U | I | I | M | A | T | E | L | G | I |
| W | G | E | C | B | O | R | E | A | D | M | L | N | O |
| N | S | O | E | Q | L | F | E | B | K | N | O | I | T |
| L | F | U | S | R | I | L | L | B | E | O | W | S | H |
| N | M | I | S | R | Y | W | A | A | Q | Z | X | K | I |
| O | O | L | P | U | R | O | F | L | O | W | E | R | S |
| C | M | L | H | J | Z | Q | U | L | M | T | S | Y | E |

# Why do you think the frog wanted to go to the castle?

_____

_____

How many nights did the frog stay with the princess?
Find the number sticker.

> Place your sticker here.

nights

How do you think the princess felt about having to share her food and bed with the frog?

_____

_____

_____

_____

_____

What did the frog turn into when the princess kissed him? Find the letter stickers to spell the word.

> Place your sticker here.

> Place your sticker here.

> Place your sticker here.

> Place your sticker here.

> Place your sticker here.

> Place your sticker here.

Who cast a spell on the prince?
Find the letter stickers to spell the word.

> Place your sticker here.

> Place your sticker here.

> Place your sticker here.

> Place your sticker here.

> Place your sticker here.

How many differences can you find between these pictures?
Find the number sticker.

There are

Place your
sticker
here.

differences.

# Help the princess get to her prince.

YOU WILL NEED: counters and a dice.

START

The princess loses her ball.
MISS A GO!

The princess makes the frog cry.
GO BACK 1 SPACE!

The witch ca: a spell.
MISS A GO

The princess loses her ball again.
GO BACK TO THE BEGINNING!

Find a friend to play with and choose who goes first.
Put your counters on the start square and take it in turns,
moving forward to get to the finish.
Watch out for trouble along the way!

The princess falls in the pond. GO BACK 1 SPACE!

The frog has eaten well. GO FORWARD 2 SPACES!

The frog makes friends with the princess. GO FORWARD 2 SPACES!

FINISH

## Which two sentences are correct?
## Tick or check the correct answers.

a. The frog dived too the bottom on the pond. ☐

b. The frog dived to the bottom of the pond. ☐

• • • • • • • • • • • • • • • • • • • • • • • • • • • • • • • •

c. A which put a spell on the prince and turned him into a frog. ☐

d. A witch put a spell on the prince and turned him into a frog. ☐

## Which word correctly completes each sentence?

overjoyed    upset

hungry    okay

The princess was [Place your sticker here.] with the frog sleeping on her pillow.

friend    enemy

chef    pet

The frog wanted to be the princess's [Place your sticker here.] .

Describe the main characters in the story.
Try to include how you think they felt.

_____

_____

_____

_____

_____

_____

_____

_____

_____

_____

_____

_____

_____

_____

_____

_____

_____

# Answers

**page 12**

Red **cape** and red **shoes**.

Red Riding Hood was going to visit **Grandma**.

The **wolf** jumped out from behind a tree.

**page 13**

Bad, jumped, screamed, cakes.

**page 14**

There were **hearts** on Grandma's nightgown.

The wolf put Grandma in a **wardrobe**.

The wolf had big **teeth**, **eyes** and **ears**.

**page 16**

oluf-wolf, ttcaego-cottage, deb-bed,

ksace-cakes, yese-eyes.

**page 18**

Sentence **5** is correct.

**page 19**

There are **6** differences.

**page 20**

a-3, b-2, c-4, d-1, e-6, f-5.

**Page 32**

**page 33**

There were **2** lazy stepsisters.

Cinderella used a **mop** to clean the floor.

**page 34**

The **prince** invited Cinderella and her sisters to the palace.

Cinderella lost her **shoe**.

**Page 35**

**page 37**

a-5, b-4, c-2, d-3, e-6, f-1.

**page 38**

Sentence **3** is correct.

**page 39**

Handsome, cakes, housework.

**page 52**

3 fairies.

The fairies brought **presents**.

The king and queen held their party at the **castle**.

**page 53**

The bad fairy said Sleeping Beauty would prick her finger on a **needle**.

Sleeping Beauty would be **eighteen** years old.

**page 54**

Everyone slept for **one hundred** years.

Path **c** leads to Sleeping Beauty.

**page 55**

There are **6** needles in the picture.

**page 56**

castles - c, fairies - b, Sleeping Beautys - d, cats - d

**page 57**

a-2, b-4, c-3, d-1, e-5, f-6.

**page 59**

Sentence **b** is correct.

He **kissed** her.

**page 72**

The princess lost her **ball**

A **frog** offered to help the princess.

The princess had to share her **pillow** and **food**.

**Page 73**

**page 74**

**3** nights.

The frog turned into a **prince**.

A **witch** cast a spell on the frog.

**page 75**

There are **5** differences.

**page 78**

Sentences **b** and **d** are correct.

Upset, friend

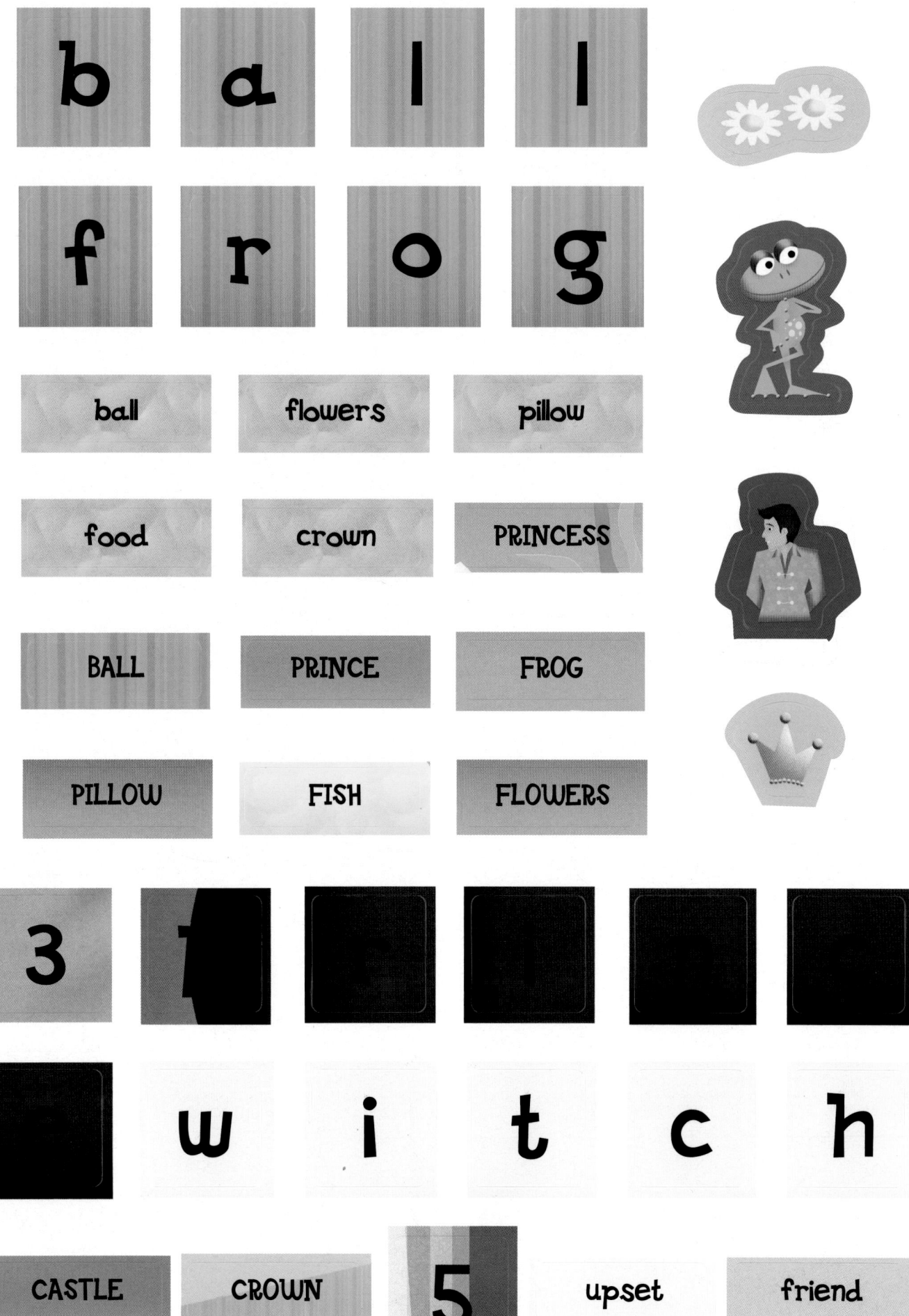